First Printing, October 2019
Tim and Colleen Browne
Quacky, Smacky & Tacky / by John Browne and Adam & Alan Tollefson
Illustrated by Alan Tollefson
Summary: Seven-year-old John Browne is given the responsibility of
raising three mallard ducklings to maturity.

ISBN-978-1-7923-1548-0
UPC - 682863731514
EAN - 0682863731514

Book design by Alan Tollefson
Manufactured in the United States of America
CG Book Printers
United States

Quacky, Smacky & "Tacky"

A Story About a Boy Raising 3 Baby Ducks to Maturity.

By John Browne. Based on a Real-Life Experience.
Illustrated by Alan Tollefson

BROWNE+BROWNE BOOKS

In the book Quacky, Smacky & Tacky, there are ten main characters. A young boy, his mother and a school teacher are human and the rest are animals.

All the characters are portrayed in somewhat of a cartoon style. The drawings are not intended to resemble the people in John's life. John looks similar to the drawings of him in the book. On the outside he is fair skinned with blonde hair, on the inside he is a warm, very conscientious young boy.

Quacky - Quacky is a drake (a male mallard) and is quite sociable and calm. Quacky often uses big words. But Smacky and Tacky also speak.

Smacky - Smacky is a hen (a female mallard) who is ladylike, and proper. Smacky doesn't really care for worms and bugs.

Tacky – Tacky is also a drake (a male mallard) and is full of mischief, often either hiding, taking chances, or just doing something silly. Tacky is the smallest of the three ducks.

All male ducks are called drakes, and all female ducks are called ducks or hens.

John - John is about 5 feet tall with blonde hair. He has a curious mind and is popular in school. John is also creative and interested in the sciences, and would like to be a biologist. He also is a loving and caring young boy.

Molly - Molly is a Canada goose. No one knows how she came to be the guardian of the ducklings. Some suspect that there is a spirit in the animal world that guides and protects its own and in this case the spirit reached out to Molly who is observant and knowledgeable of the animal ways.
A goose can also be ferocious when it is being protective.

Miss Prichard - Miss Prichard is John's school teacher. She is smart, friendly and caring, and enjoys all her students. She gets to know each one of them well so that everyone feels they are an important member of the class.

John's Mom - John's mother is a lovely woman. She supports John in everything he does and helps whenever he asks her.

The Hawk - In the real world, hawks and eagles will prey on ducks whenever possible. Luckily the hawk in this book had problems of its own.

The Fox - A fox is an omnivore (eats food of both plant and animal origin). A fox is a common predator of ducklings. They are also very sly (sneaky, crafty, clever or tricky). Sly as a fox is a common saying.

Mr. Raccoon - Raccoons are primarily nocturnal (awake and active at night) and because they commonly eat human garbage, you often find them in populated areas. They also make a diet of small animals, birds, frogs and snakes. In the mornings, raccoons will find a hollow log, crawl space under a house or a pile of brush to sleep in.

MOLLY

"I'm Molly, a Canada goose. I made a vow years ago to keep a watchful eye on a young boy who was raising three distant relatives of mine. My concern was their safety. So here is the story . . . it begins at a school on a warm spring day in May. Previously, twenty-five mallard eggs were delivered from a local farm to the school as part of a biology project. After the eggs hatched, three of the ducklings were given to Miss Prichard's class and placed in a small pen."

"John was happy that he was chosen and immediately began to read about everything he would need to do. First, John made a box that was open on the top and he filled it with grass clippings. John also included a small dish of water.

This morning, John's mother is taking him to school to pick up the ducklings and bring them home."

MOLLY

"Mom, I read that ducklings feel safe in small, enclosed places so this box should be nice and cozy for them," said John.

MOLLY

"John proudly walked from his mother's car carrying the box he made for the ducklings and excitedly entered the classroom."

"Good morning Miss Prichard," John said.
"Good morning John. That looks like a wonderful way to safely take our ducklings home," said Miss Prichard.
"Have you thought of a name for each of them?" she asked.

"Yes, I have. The biggest one is Quacky, the smallest one is Tacky, the other one is Smacky," said John.

"It's nice to have such cute names," said Smacky.

"Yikes! Are we going to tip over?" asked Tacky.
"No Tacky," said Quacky, "I think we're just turning into
John's driveway. We're almost home."

"Hmm, Smacky doesn't seem to like the food," John thought.

"It looks to me like young John noticed Smacky doesn't like bugs and worms. I hope he brings her something else to eat," Quacky thought.

"John was an alert and conscientious boy. He had noticed that Smacky wasn't eating so he did a little research. John discovered that many ducklings like to eat finely chopped fruits and vegetables."

"Here you go Smacky. I bet you'll like these," said John.
"I have raspberries, blueberries and carrots."

"A few weeks later, John introduced the ducklings to a new pen he was building outside. It will be made of wire mesh and will have a roof over one end, a pan of water, and a pan with bugs, worms and of course, vegetables."

"This is quite splendid and exhilarating," said Quacky.

"Yup, sure is. Look how fast I can run," yelled Tacky, as he ran far, far away from his siblings. "Tacky, Tacky," yelled Smacky, "You'd better hurry back. You don't know what creature might be hiding waiting to attack you."

"The summer days flew by as fast as a humming bird* flaps its wings. The ducklings were growing quickly and every day they ate and played in the yard. Occasionally, they looked to the sky when something caught their attention."

MOLLY

"Look at the ducks," Quacky whispered.
"Isn't that exciting?
   I think those are ducks just like us but a little older." Smacky, looking up said, "Oh my, they are beautiful."

*A humming bird flaps its wings about 10 to 15 times each second.

"John heard loud chirping and ran over to the pen just in time to scare a Hawk away with help from all the little birds."

"Oh dear, look over by the fence, it's a hawk. There are all kinds of birds that seem to be attacking it," said Smacky. "Hurry up Tacky, run for the pen quickly," screamed Quacky.

"Don't worry Tacky, you're going to make it. And this wire roof will keep you safe from hawks," John said in a reassuring tone. "I will stay with you tonight to make sure that hawk doesn't come back."

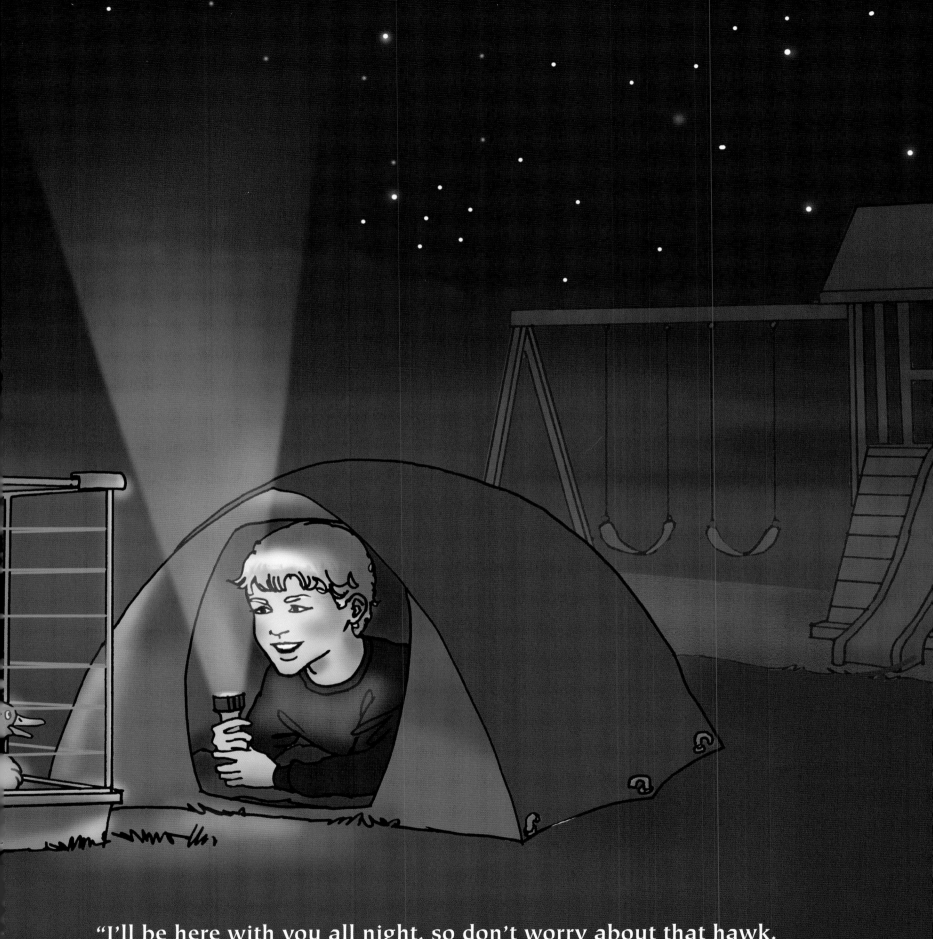

"I'll be here with you all night, so don't worry about that hawk.
It won't be back," John said confidently.

"Okay Quacky, it's your turn to dive* for food," John said with excitement.
"I have worms, minnows and vegetables in the pool for you."

"Can you crawl around like this and look for food?" John asked.
"Oh Smacky, it looks like you've finally decided to eat worms."

*dive. For mallards and other puddle ducks, this kind of diving for food is called "dabbling."

MOLLY

"John was still in his pajamas the next morning when a thunderstorm began. The dark clouds quickly consumed the whole sky. Lightning stretched along the horizon and thunder rumbled. Together, the wind and rain were damaging the duck's pen."

"There you go. The lightning has stopped and I will tie down this new top that will keep you dry. I'll stay with you until the storm is over.

You'll be okay, don't worry," John said thoughtfully.

"It was a beautiful day in late August. Several weeks had passed and Quacky, Smacky and Tacky had grown considerably. John heard noises and lots of quacking so he quickly ran outside and found a fox jumping on the pen. Smacky and Tacky were huddled away from the fox. Quacky was laying down inside looking injured."

MOLLY

"Get out of here fox! Oh Quacky, what has happened to you?" John said with fear in his voice.

"Mom, mom, can we take Quacky to a doctor right away? He was attacked by a fox and I think he's badly hurt," John pleaded.

MOLLY

"John and his mom took Quacky to the veterinarian. The veterinarian looked Quacky over thoroughly," and said - "Quacky has been hurt and is pretty frightened, but in a few days he'll be just fine."

"Oh boy, we almost lost a good friend today didn't we? That was scary. I'm glad Quacky is going to be okay but he will have to rest for a few days," John said.

"It is now September and Quacky has healed just fine. The trees are changing to their fall colors. Quacky, Smacky and Tacky are acting as though they don't quite know what to do. Flocks of ducks are flying over every day and the three ducks watch them all the time."

John said with tears in his eyes, "I love all three of you and I know I will miss you forever, but you have to fly away and join all the other wild mallard ducks."

"Well Quacky and Tacky, it's time for us to join a flock of ducks flying south," said Smacky. Turning in John's direction, they quacked, "We love you too John and we'll try to come back some day."

"Fly away now and enjoy your new life," John yelled after them. "Remember, try to come back someday."

MOLLY

"John seemed to understand exactly what they were saying. They quacked a few more times and then flapped their wings, rising straight up off the ground as puddle ducks* can do. Once up in the air, Quacky, Smacky and Tacky made their way toward a flock of mallard ducks flying overhead."

* Mallards are one species of puddle ducks. Puddle ducks are able to launch themselves directly upward when taking off.

Interesting Facts About Migratory Birds

Ducks do not have teeth but can enjoy finely chopped fruits, vegetables or greens. Small insects and worms make good treats, as well.

Mallard ducks are the most common and recognizable wild ducks in the Northern Hemisphere. You'll find them near ponds, marshes, streams and lakes, where they feed on plants, invertebrates, fish, and insects. Mallards are dabbling, or surface-feeding ducks because they eat by tipping underwater for food—head down, feet and tail in the air, rather than diving. Mallards also forage and graze for food on land.

The male mallard duck, called a drake, has a glossy green head, a white ring around its neck and a rich, chestnut-brown breast. The mottled brown female mallard looks somewhat dull next to the drake's brighter coloring.

The mallard duck's outer feathers are waterproof, thanks to oil that's secreted from a "preen" gland near the tail. Ducks will spread the oil on their feathers with their beaks. Beneath this tightly packed waterproof layer of feathers lies a soft, warm layer of feathers called down. Twice a year, mallards molt, or shed, their flight feathers, temporarily grounding the birds for several weeks until the feathers grow back.

Mallards fly in groups called flocks. Like most migratory birds, mallards fly in a "V" formation creating wind reduction, and conserving energy, for the following birds. The lead bird is periodically replaced by others during long flights. During winter migration, mallards fly south in search of warm weather, often resting at the same spots year after year.

A female mallard lays up to a dozen eggs in a nest on the ground near water. Often in a small depression or tree hole. The hen lines the nest with warm down plucked from her undercoat. Soon after birth, baby ducks, called ducklings, open their eyes. A little more than a day after hatching, ducklings can run, swim, and forage for food on their own. They stay in the nest for less than a month. Outside the nest, the ducklings stay close by the mother for safety, often following behind her in a neat, single-file line.

If a predator is lurking nearby, a mother mallard will pretend to be injured to distract it from her ducklings.

Mated pairs migrate to northern parts of their range, breed and build nests on the ground or in a protected tree cavity. They normally lay about a dozen eggs. The incubation period lasts just under a month. After incubation, the eggs all hatch the same day. When the ducklings hatch, their eyes are open, and they already have feathers.

They will stay in the nest for about 10 hours. Then, often in the early morning, the mother will lead them to water, but before doing so, the mother will spread her own oil over each of the ducklings which will prevent them from sinking.

It will take 60 days for a duckling to fledge. ("Fledge" means - to develop large enough wing feathers that enable them to fly.)

Mallards are territorial during much of the early nesting period, but once incubation is well underway, males abandon the nest and join a flock of other males.

• A common nickname for the female mallard is "Suzy."

• Female ducks have a tendency to breed near the place where they were hatched.

• A group of ducklings is called a "brood."

• A mallard's diet consists of aquatic vegetation, insects, worms, and grain crops like wheat and corn.

• A duck can dip its head under the water and forage for plants on the bottom. This is the feeding technique it prefers and executes most often.

• Mallard ducklings are precocial, meaning they know how to swim and feed right after they are hatched.

• Males and females pair up in the fall for the winter and remain paired until the spring mating season.

• Young ducks are able to breed anywhere from 17 to 30 weeks of age depending on whether they are a small duck or a larger breed of duck.

• Migrating mallards can travel great distances. Though we still don't fully understand how they find their way, ducks, like all migratory birds, use the sun, the stars, mountain ranges, rivers and roads to guide them. It is also believed that in the bird's eyes or brain, there is a small magnetic zone (magnetic minerals) that works like a small compass.

• Adult mallard ducks weigh 2 to 3 pounds

• Adults will measure about 20″ to 26″ in length

• Adults can fly as fast as 47 miles per hour

• The mallard has a life span of 5 to 10 years

• The mallard has a wingspan of 2.7 feet to 3.2 feet

• Geese, cranes and swans, need to learn to find their way by following their parents while migrating the first time. Ducks do not.

• Scientific Name: Anas platyrhynchos (Latin name)

• Type: Birds

• Diet: Omnivore (An animal or person that eats food of both plant and animal origin)

Top 10 Tips on Caring for Mallard Ducklings

Proven ways to nurture orphan or "found wildlife" ducklings and prepare them to fly and join in a migration.

One. Brooder Box for Baby Ducks: set up in your house, garage or shed, a sturdy cardboard box, a large plastic storage container, a galvanized tub, or dog crate lined with old towels, plastic and newspaper (with rubber shelf liner over paper/plastic so wobbly ducklings' legs won't slip) and to absorb water. Include a heat lamp with 100-watt bulb to start (not too close to ducklings), and a shallow bowl of water, and a shallow bowl of food; You'll need a thermometer to check the temperature, which needs to be 90 degrees during the duckling's first week. You can lower the temperature one degree each day (7 degrees per week) until the temperature in the garage or house is close to or the same as the environment. Do not overheat the ducklings. Raise the lamp and bulb wattage as they stop sleeping under it, and as they grow older. But ducklings have to stay warm.

Two. Safe, Predator-Proof Environment: Be sure your brooder box is protected from the weather and predators; Cover your brooder box to protect the ducklings from curious children and family pets. Advise children to handle ducklings gently and carefully and always with adult supervision.

Three. Chick Starter Food: Use duckling food (unmediated) from local Co-op or feed store. You can also feed ducklings starter crumbs, chopped grass, fresh or dandelion greens, weeds, bugs, worms, kale, peas, etc. Add a sprinkle of brewer's yeast or raw oats on top of the food. Sprinkle with a little water to moisten. That helps the duckling build strong bones and a little water to moisten. Dispose of any wet feed daily and add fresh food. Interact with your ducklings often during feeding, give them treats and you'll have them eating out of your hand before you know it!

Four. Plenty of Water: a week-old duckling drinks about a half-gallon of water a week, by seven weeks old, ducklings drink a half gallon of water a day, so be sure always plenty of clean fresh water available. Refresh the water often, minimum daily and clean bowl.

Five. Adult Duck Food: after about 16 weeks, use only adult duck food (not food for baby chickens), but be sure the ducklings have access to food 24/7, available whenever they are hungry, as they grow so quickly at this stage. Avoid all human food for your ducklings, as it can make them sick.

Six. Outdoor Space: after 3-5 weeks with average 70 degrees temperatures, move outside to enjoy warm sunny days in your well-ventilated duck pen, house or coop. This would be a larger outdoor space, predator-proof (from storms, other animals and large predatory birds like hawks) and fenced in, with straw on floor, water bowl deep enough for duckling's entire bill to submerge to keep mucous membranes moist, but not too deep where they could fall into and possibly drown, and large enough so ducks can fully expand their wings and groom. They can take short swims at this stage in small pool, but always supervised and dry them off gently. By 8-10 weeks, they are fully feathered but still need heat. Keep pen dry and clean, so change bedding often.

Seven. Duck Love to Swim: set up a kiddie swimming pool after 2.5 months after fully feathered, with warm water, deep enough to get their entire heads submerged to clean out their nostrils and where can fully float in/swim in pool and a ramp into and out of pool (until large enough to get in/out of pool on their own). Ducks clean themselves, so no need to wash them (if oil or other debris on ducklings, use Dawn®). By now, the ducks are several months old and can produce oil to waterproof their wings.

Eight. Water Availability: always have enough drinking water available when ducklings eat. At night just water, no food, but always water. Never have just food and no water, as the duckling needs the water to digest food and not choke.

Nine. Playtime-Fun in the Yard: Enjoy your new friends as they play together and with you in your yard, as they chase you around the yard and crawl on you as you lay in the grass. Balance between enjoying them too much (handling them) as to not imprint on humans too much, as you want to make sure your ducklings grow up into independent healthy adults.

Ten. Ready to Fly: After 5-6 months of raising the ducklings, they now have the ability to fly and join in a migration. Can be both a time of joy and sadness, as you've gotten close to your ducks as friends, but you know it is best for the wildlife to return to their natural wild habitat. The ducks get close to you as well, so they may need some encouragement (some take up permanent residence) to leave, to get them to fly away from your yard, back to nature and joining fellow ducks in a migration.